Arranged for all portable keyboards *by Kenneth Baker.*

THE COMPLETE KEYBOARD PLAYER

JEROME KERN

Wise Publications
London/New York/Sydney

Exclusive distributors:
Music Sales Limited
8/9 Frith Street, London W1V 5TZ, England.
Music Sales Pty Limited
120 Rothschild Avenue, Rosebery, NSW 2018, Australia.

This book © Copyright 1990 by
Wise Publications
Order No.AM79294
UK ISBN 0.7119.2210.1

Designed by Pearce Marchbank Studio
Arranged by Kenneth Baker
Compiled by Peter Evans
Music processed by Musicprint

Photographs courtesy of:
Pictorial Press

Music Sales' complete catalogue lists thousands of
titles and is free from your local music shop, or direct from
Music Sales Limited. Please send £1 in stamps for postage to
Music Sales Limited, 8/9 Frith Street, London W1V 5TZ.

Printed in the United Kingdom by

J.B. Offset Printers (Marks Tey) Limited, Marks Tey, Essex.

DEARLY BELOVED

Music by Jerome Kern
Words by Johnny Mercer

Suggested registration: flute
Rhythm: beguine (or rhumba)
Tempo: medium (♩ = 126)

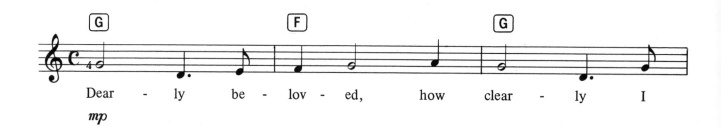

Dear - ly be - lov - ed, how clear - ly I

mp

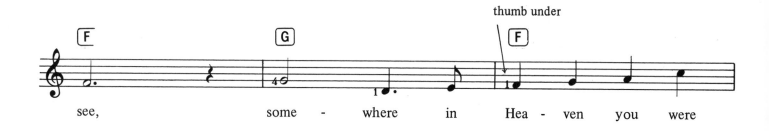

see, some - where in Hea - ven you were

thumb under

fash - ioned for me. An - gel eyes _____

flute to clarinet

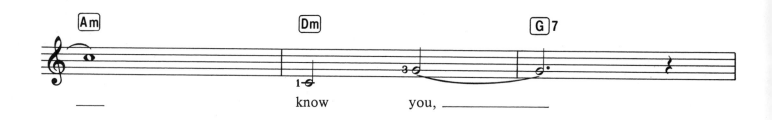

_____ know you, _____

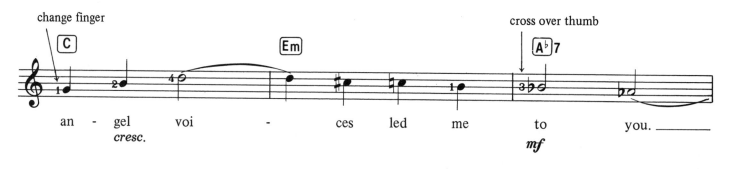

an - gel voi - ces led me to you. _____

change finger

cresc.

cross over thumb

mf

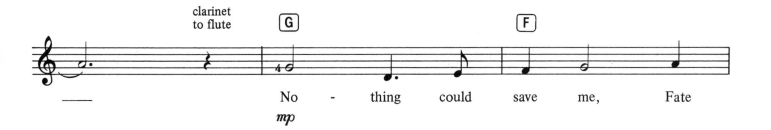

clarinet to flute

No - thing could save me, Fate

mp

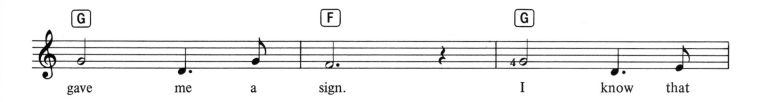

gave me a sign. I know that

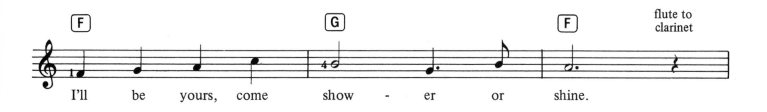

flute to clarinet

I'll be yours, come show - er or shine.

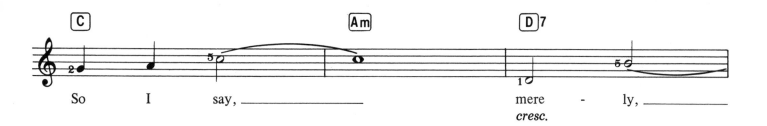

So I say, _____ mere - ly, _____

cresc.

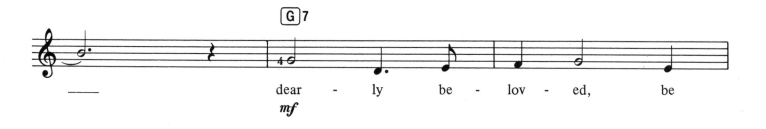

dear - ly be - lov - ed, be

mf

mine. _____ stop rhythm

5

I'VE TOLD EV'RY LITTLE STAR

Music by Jerome Kern
Words by Oscar Hammerstein II

Suggested registration: musical box (or flute with sustain)
Rhythm: swing
Tempo: medium (♩ = 120)

I've told ev-'ry lit-tle star, just how sweet I
mp

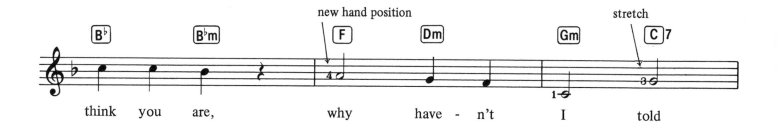

think you are, why have-n't I told

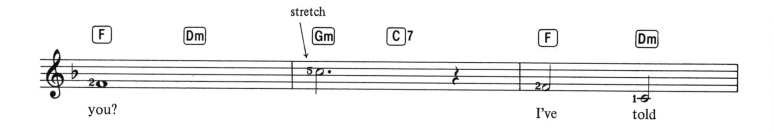

you? I've told

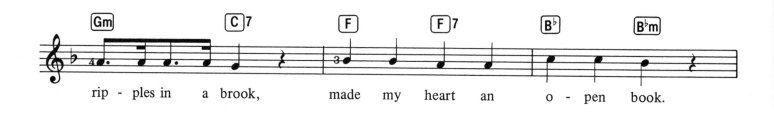

rip-ples in a brook, made my heart an o-pen book.

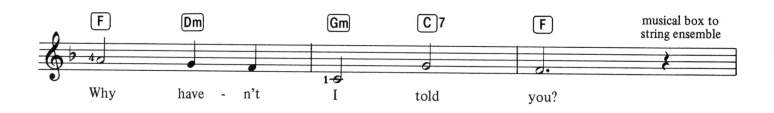

Why have-n't I told you?

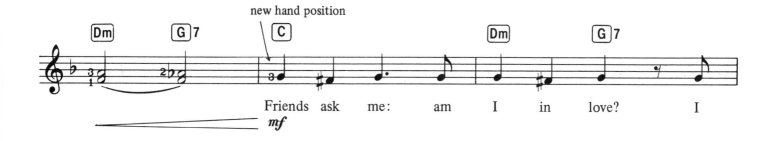

Friends ask me: am I in love? I

al - ways ans - wer "yes." Might as well con -

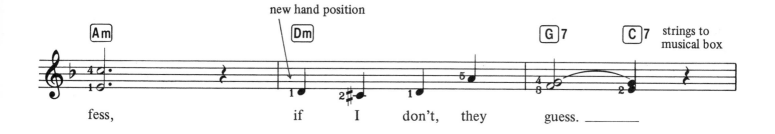

fess, if I don't, they guess. _____

May - be you may know it too, oh, my dar - ling,

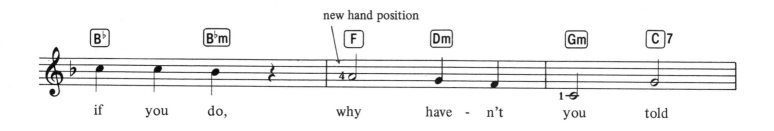

if you do, why have - n't you told

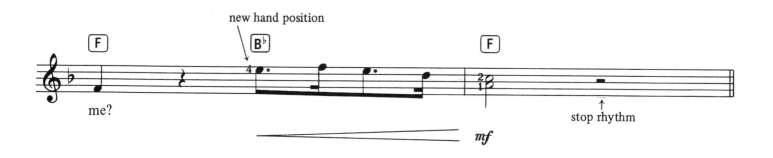

me?

7

LONG AGO AND FAR AWAY

Music by Jerome Kern
Words by Ira Gershwin

Suggested registration: violin solo
Rhythm: beguine (or rhumba)
Tempo: medium (♩ = 112)

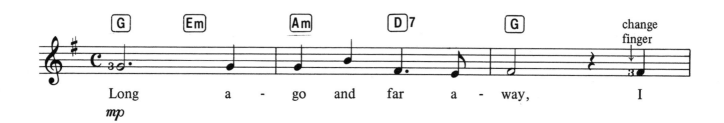

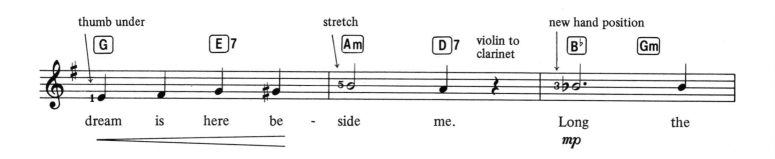

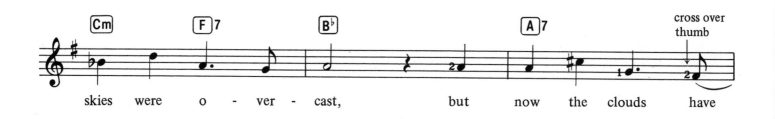

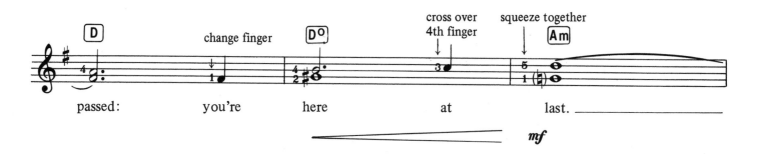

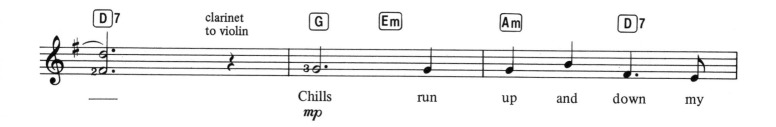

Chills run up and down my
mp

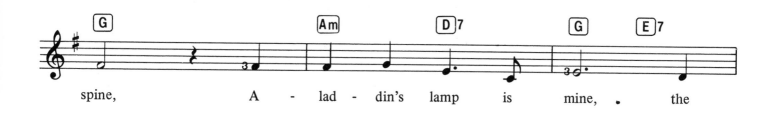

spine, A - lad - din's lamp is mine, . the

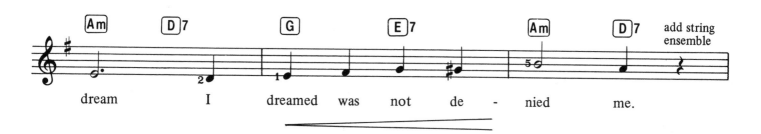

dream I dreamed was not de - nied me.

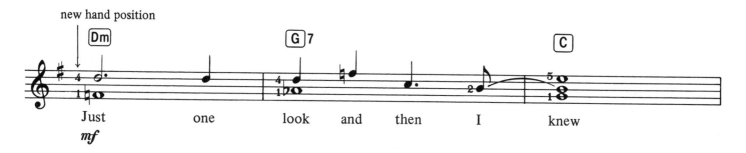

Just one look and then I knew
mf

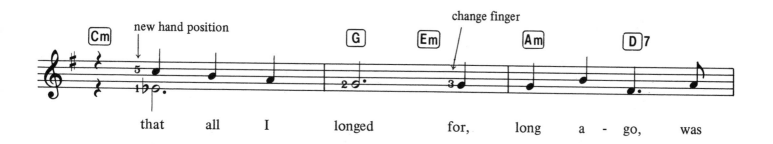

that all I longed for, long a - go, was

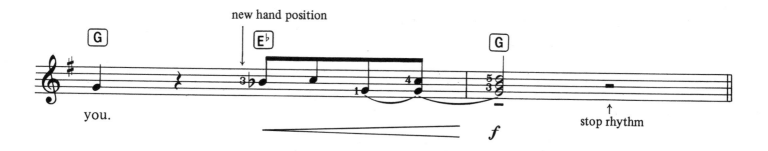

you.
f

A FINE ROMANCE

Music by Jerome Kern
Words by Dorothy Fields

Suggested registration: piano
Rhythm: swing
Tempo: fast (♩ = 168)
Synchro-start on

A   fine   ro - mance!   With

mf

no   kiss - es!   A   fine

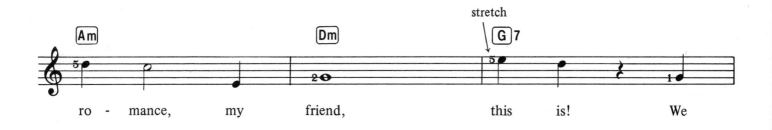

ro - mance,   my   friend,   this   is!   We

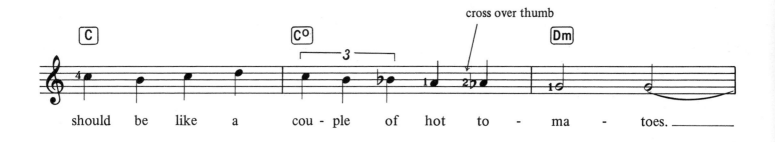

should   be   like   a   cou - ple   of   hot   to - ma - toes. ____

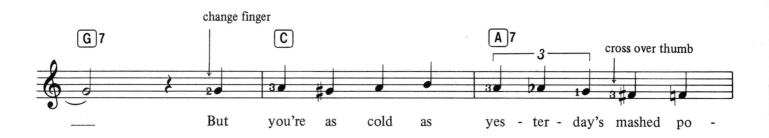

____   But   you're as   cold   as   yes - ter - day's mashed po -

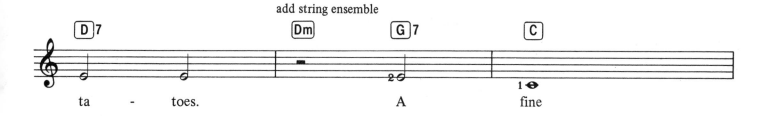

add string ensemble

ta - toes. A fine

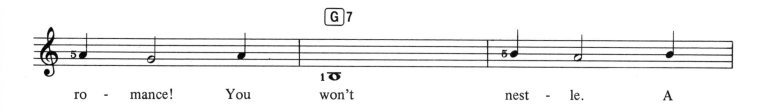

ro - mance! You won't nest - le. A

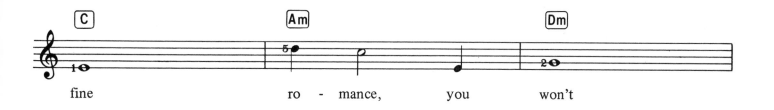

fine ro - mance, you won't

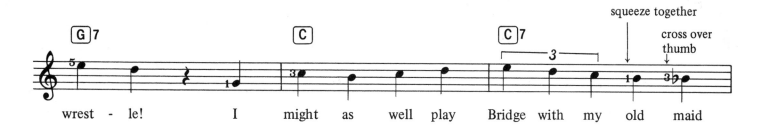

squeeze together

cross over
thumb

wrest - le! I might as well play Bridge with my old maid

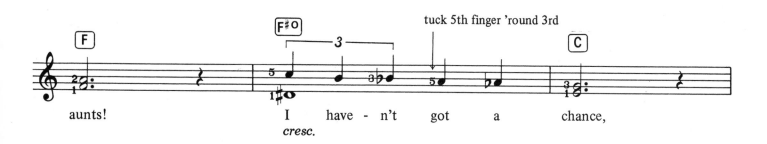

tuck 5th finger 'round 3rd

aunts! I have - n't got a chance,

cresc.

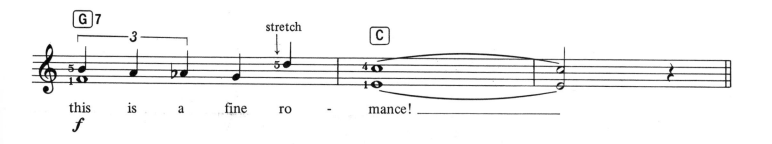

stretch

this is a fine ro - mance! _____

f

11

YESTERDAYS

Music by Jerome Kern
Words by Otto Harbach

Suggested registration: vibraphone
Rhythm: bossa nova
Tempo: medium (♩ = 112)

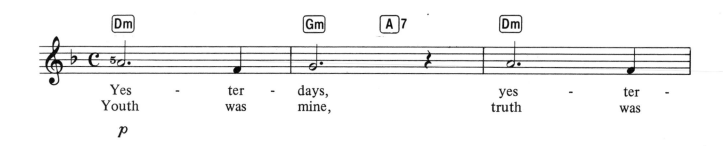

Yes - ter - days, yes - ter -
Youth was mine, truth was

days. Days I knew as hap - py, sweet se -
mine. Joy - ous, free and flam - ing life, for -

ques - ter'd days. Old - en days,
sooth, was mine. Sad am I,

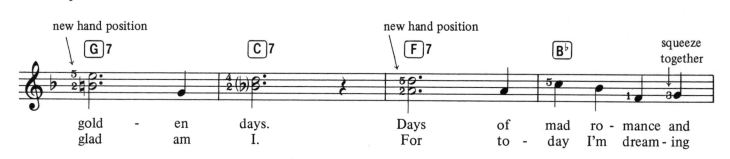

gold - en days. Days of mad ro - mance and
glad am I. For to - day I'm dream - ing

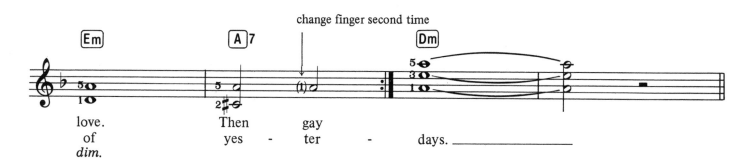

love. Then gay
of yes - ter - days. _____

I WON'T DANCE

Music by Jerome Kern
Words by Oscar Hammerstein II, Dorothy Fields

Suggested registration: clarinet
Rhythm: swing
Tempo: fast (♩ = 176)

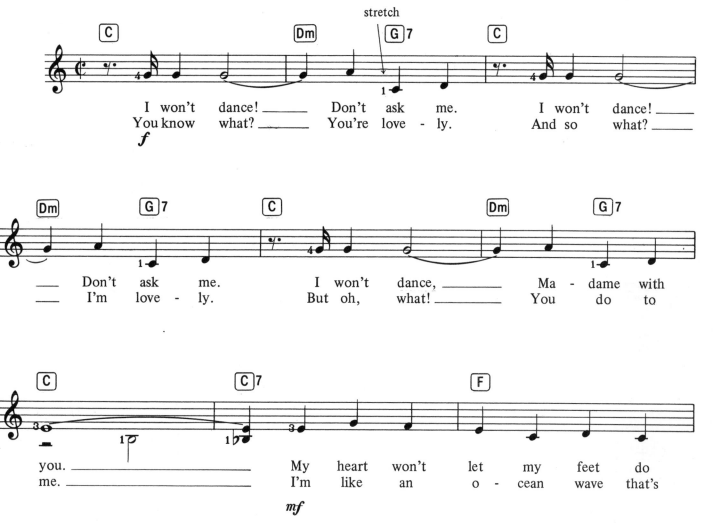

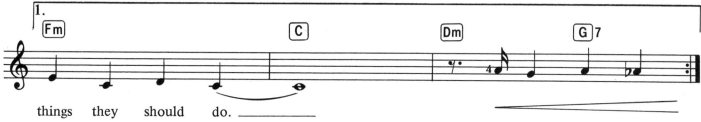

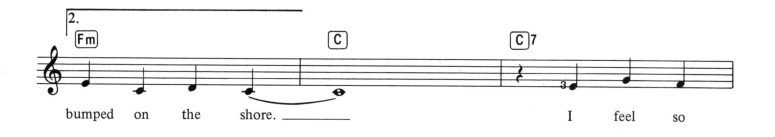

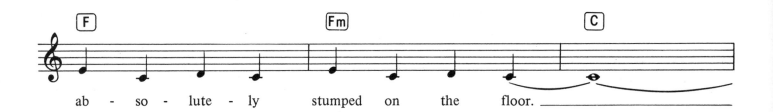

ab - so - lute - ly   stumped   on   the   floor. _____

add trombone
(or brass ensemble)

thumb under

When   you   dance   you're   charm - ing   and   you're

mp

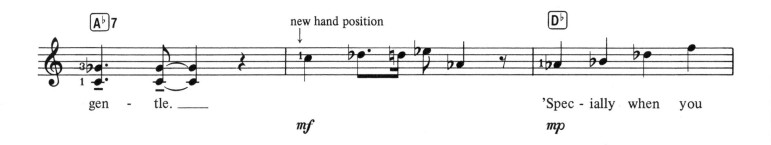

new hand position

gen - tle. _____   'Spec - ially   when   you

mf   *mp*

new hand position

do   the   'Con - ti - nen - tal'. _____

mf

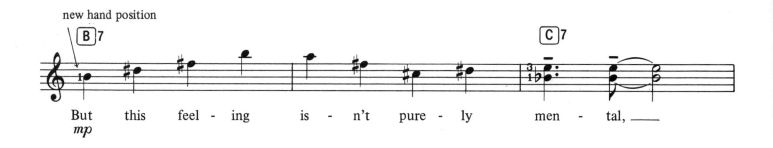

new hand position

But   this   feel - ing   is - n't   pure - ly   men - tal, _____

mp

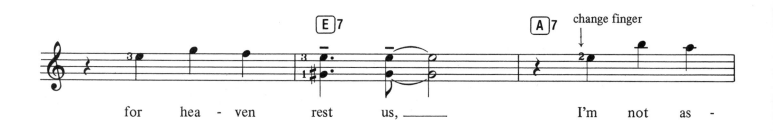

change finger

for   hea - ven   rest   us, _____   I'm   not   as -

bes - tos.＿＿ And that's why: I won't dance!＿＿

＿ Why should I? I won't dance!＿＿ How could I?

I won't dance!＿＿ Mer - ci beau - coup!＿＿＿＿

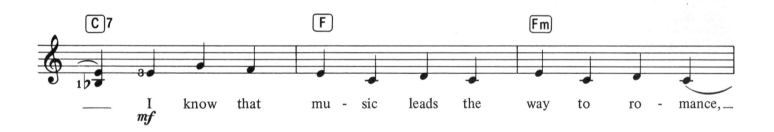

＿ I know that mu - sic leads the way to ro - mance,＿

so if I hold you in my

arms, I won't dance!＿＿

I'M OLD FASHIONED

Music by Jerome Kern
Words by Johnny Mercer

Suggested registration: string ensemble
Rhythm: beguine (or rhumba)
Tempo: medium (♩ = 126)

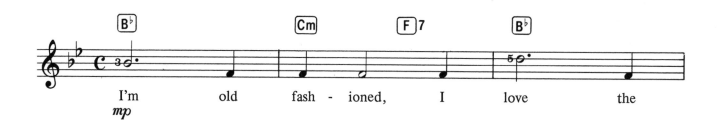

I'm old fash - ioned, I love the

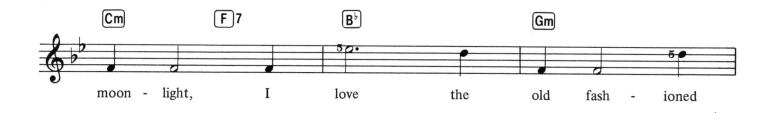

moon - light, I love the old fash - ioned

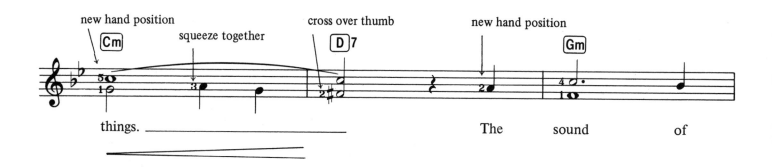

things. _____ The sound of

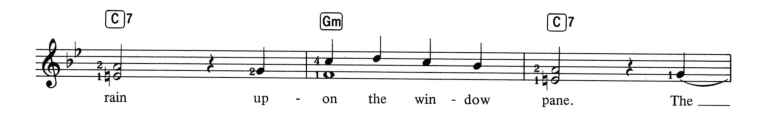

rain up - on the win - dow pane. The ____

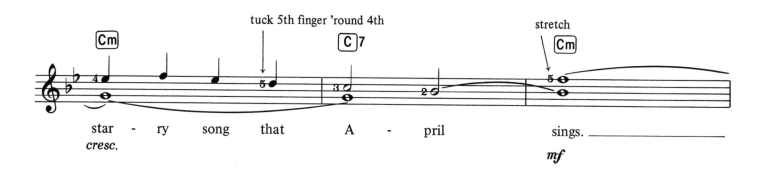

star - ry song that A - pril sings. _____

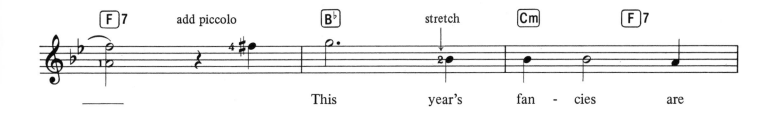

add piccolo   stretch

This year's fan - cies are

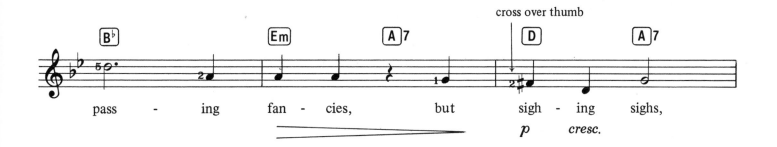

cross over thumb

pass - ing fan - cies, but sigh - ing sighs,

p   *cresc.*

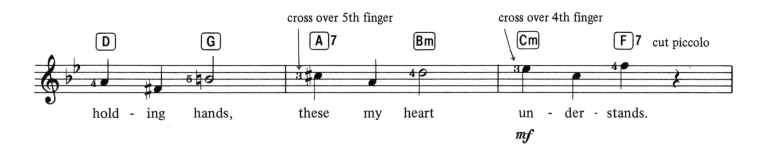

cross over 5th finger   cross over 4th finger   cut piccolo

hold - ing hands, these my heart un - der - stands.

mf

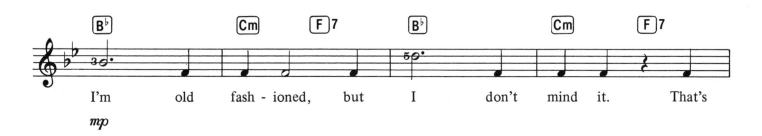

I'm old fash - ioned, but I don't mind it. That's

mp

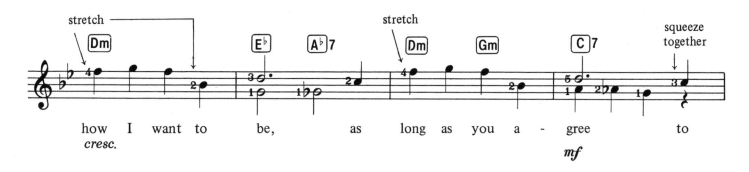

stretch   stretch   squeeze together

how I want to be, as long as you a - gree to

cresc.   *mf*

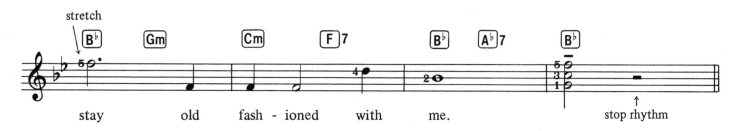

stretch

stay old fash - ioned with me.

stop rhythm

THE FOLKS WHO LIVE ON THE HILL

Music by Jerome Kern
Words by Oscar Hammerstein II

Suggested registration: guitar
Rhythm: swing
Tempo: slow (♩ = 84)

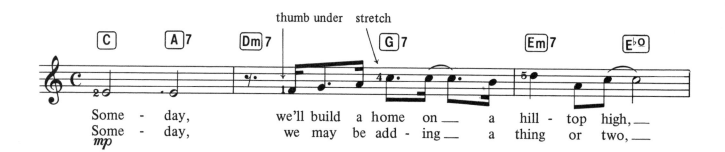

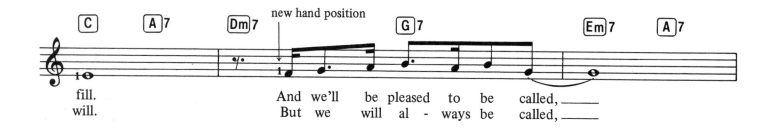

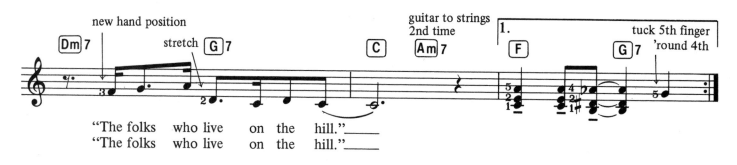

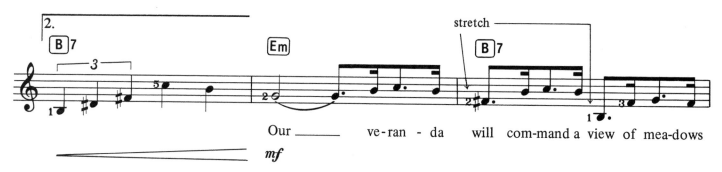

green, the sort of view that seems to want to be seen. _____

strings to guitar

And when the kids grow up and leave us, we'll sit and look at ___ that

mp

squeeze together new hand position

same old view, ___ just we two, ___ Dar - by and Joan, ___ who

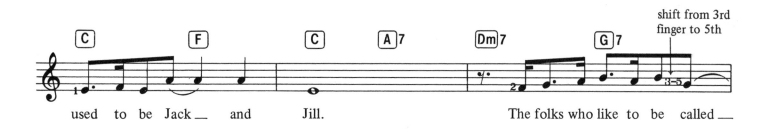

used to be Jack ___ and Jill. The folks who like to be called ___

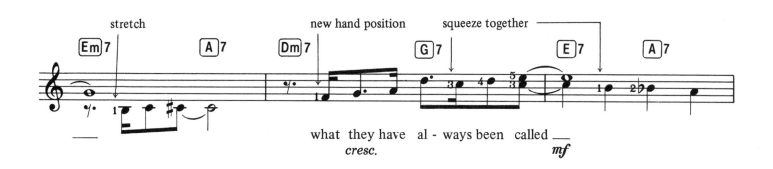

stretch new hand position squeeze together

___ what they have al - ways been called ___

cresc. *mf*

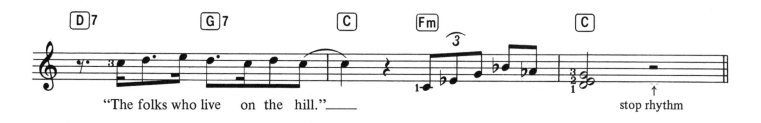

"The folks who live on the hill." _____

stop rhythm

THEY DIDN'T BELIEVE ME

Music by Jerome Kern
Words by Herbert Reynolds

Suggested registration: piano
Rhythm: beguine (or rhumba)
Tempo: medium (♩ = 108)
Synchro-start on

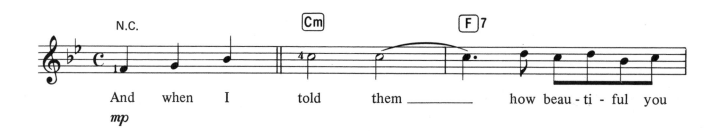

And when I told them _____ how beau-ti-ful you

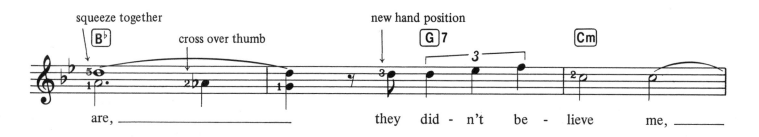

are, _____ they did-n't be-lieve me, _____

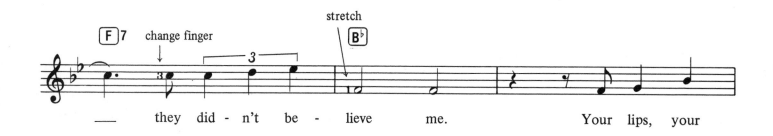

_____ they did-n't be-lieve me. Your lips, your

eyes, your cheeks, your hair are in a class be-yond com-

pare. You're the love-li-est girl _____ that one could

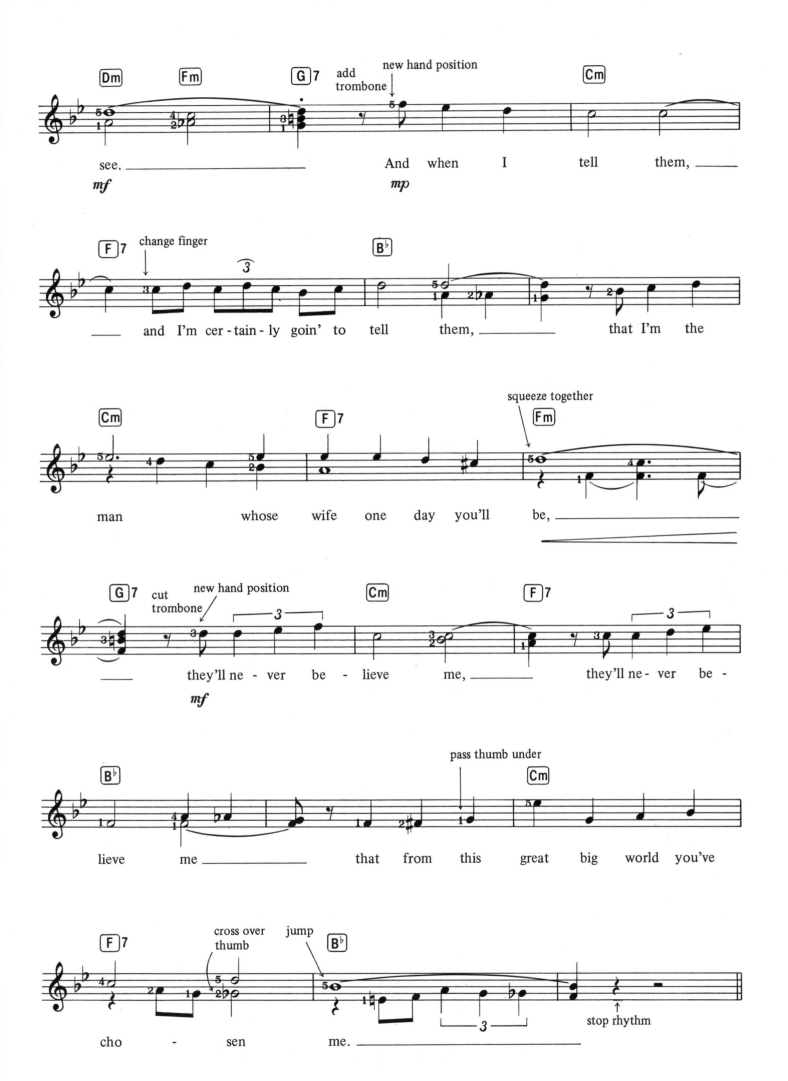

PICK YOURSELF UP

Music by Jerome Kern
Words by Dorothy Fields

Suggested registration: brass ensemble
Rhythm: swing
Tempo: fast (♩ = 184)

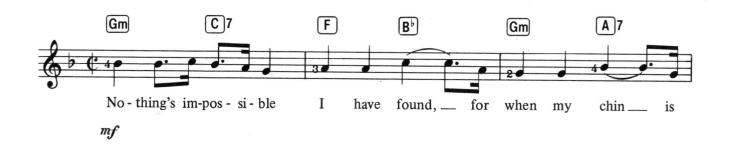

No - thing's im - pos - si - ble   I   have   found, __   for   when   my   chin __   is

on   the   ground, __   I   pick   my - self   up,   dust   my - self   off,

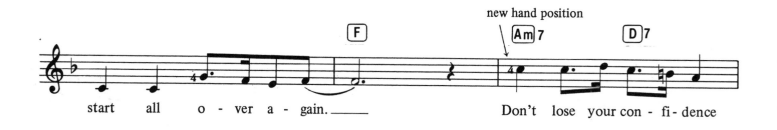

start   all   o - ver   a - gain. ____   Don't   lose   your   con - fi - dence

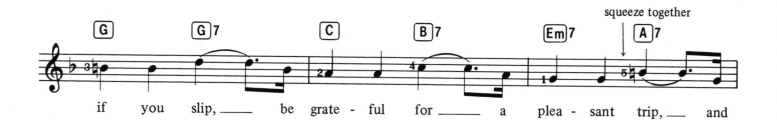

if   you   slip, __   be   grate - ful   for ____   a   plea - sant   trip, __   and

pick   your - self   up,   dust   your - self   off,   start   all   o - ver   a - gain.

add piccolo

Work like a soul in - spir - ed, till the

mp

bat - tle of the day is won. ___ You may be sick and

stretch

tir - ed, but you'll be a man, my son! ___

cresc.

cut piccolo

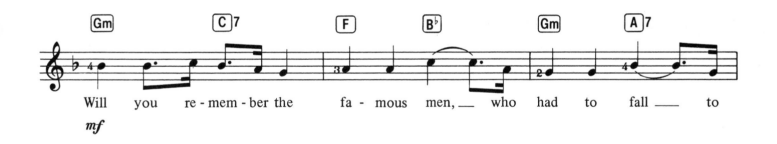

Will you re - mem - ber the fa - mous men, ___ who had to fall ___ to

mf

rise a - gain? ___ So take a deep breath, dust your - self off,

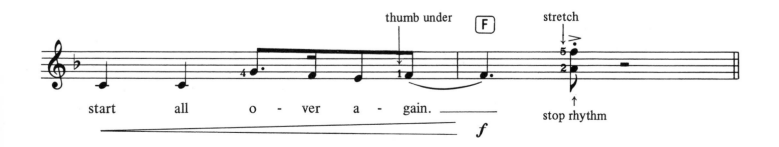

thumb under   stretch

start all o - ver a - gain. ___   *f*

stop rhythm

ALL THE THINGS YOU ARE

Music by Jerome Kern
Words by Oscar Hammerstein II

Suggested registration: guitar
Rhythm: bossa nova
Tempo: medium (♩ = 108)

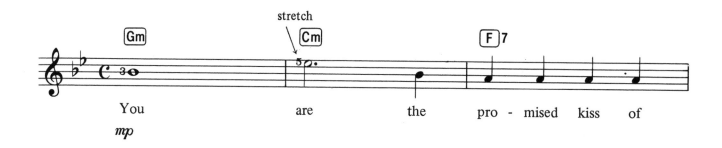

You are the pro - mised kiss of

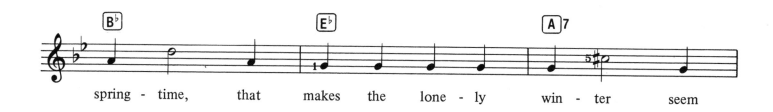

spring - time, that makes the lone - ly win - ter seem

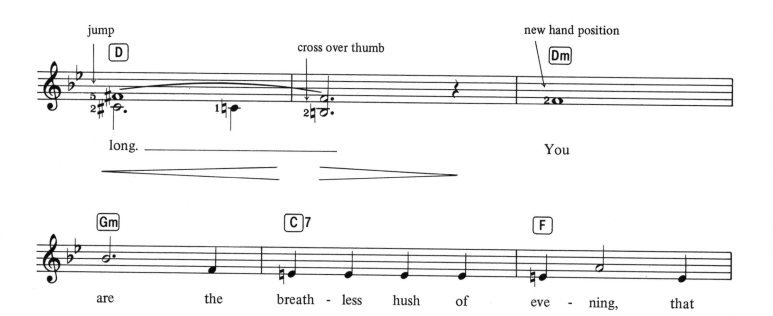

long. _____ You

are the breath - less hush of eve - ning, that

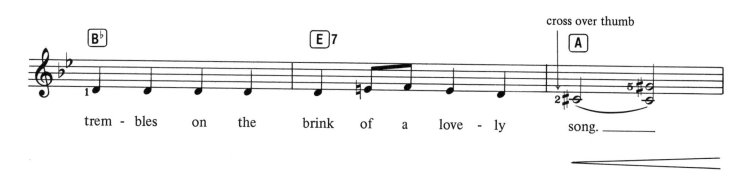

trem - bles on the brink of a love - ly song. _____

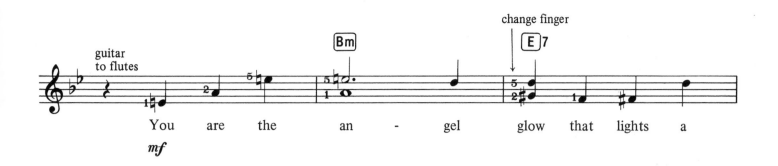

You are the an - gel glow that lights a

star, _____ the dear - est things I

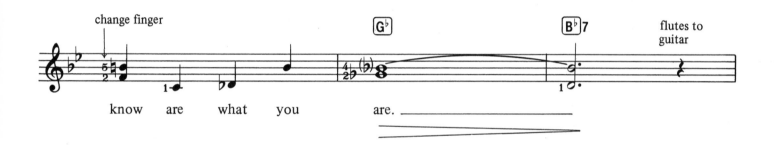

know are what you are. _____

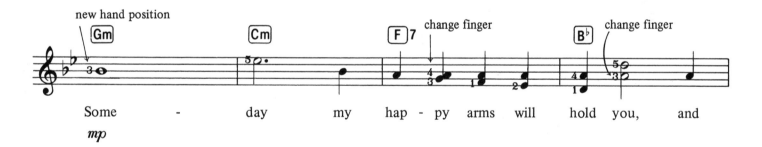

Some - day my hap - py arms will hold you, and

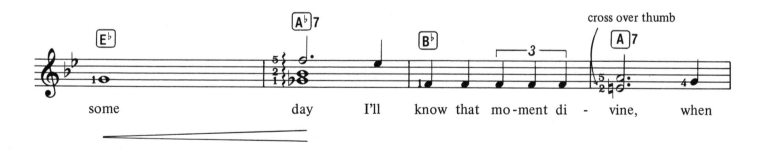

some day I'll know that mo - ment di - vine, when

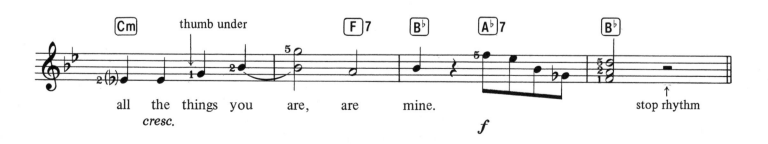

all the things you are, are mine.

CAN'T HELP LOVIN' DAT MAN

Music by Jerome Kern
Words by Oscar Hammerstein II

Suggested registration: oboe
Rhythm: swing
Tempo: fairly slow (♩ = 76)

Fish got to swim, __ and birds got to fly. __ I got to love __ one

p

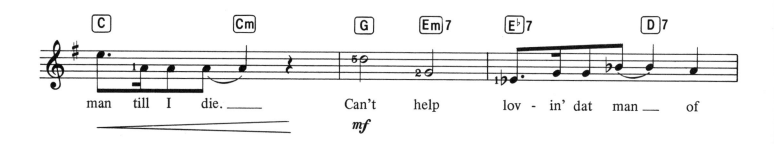

man till I die. _____ Can't help lov - in' dat man __ of

mf

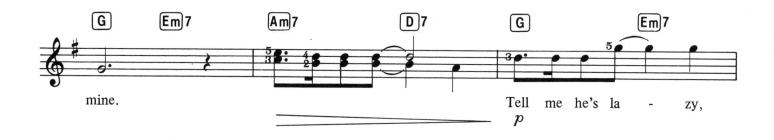

mine. Tell me he's la - zy,

p

tell me he's slow. __ Tell me I'm cra - zy, may - be I know. __

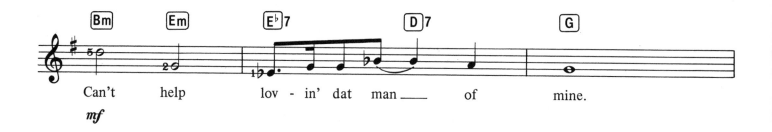

Can't help lov - in' dat man ___ of mine.

mf

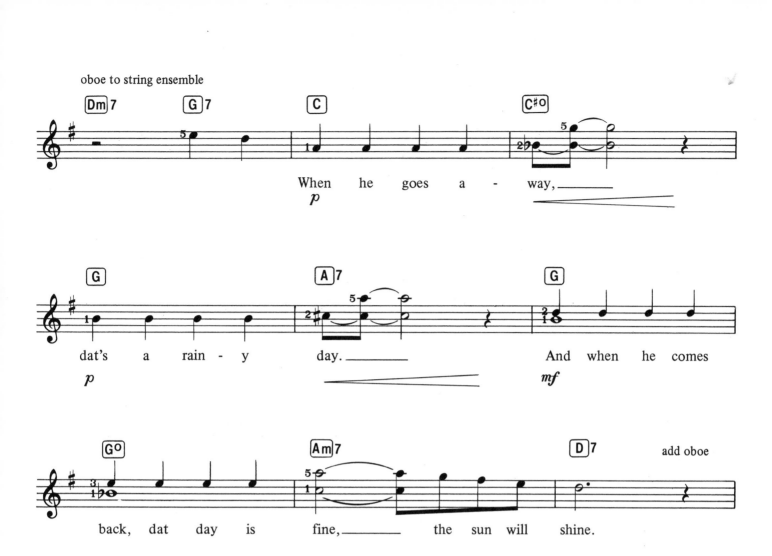

When he goes a - way, dat's a rain - y day. And when he comes back, dat day is fine, the sun will shine.

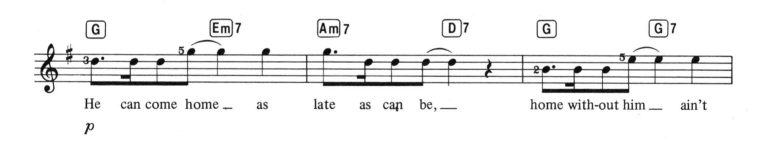

He can come home as late as can be, home with-out him ain't

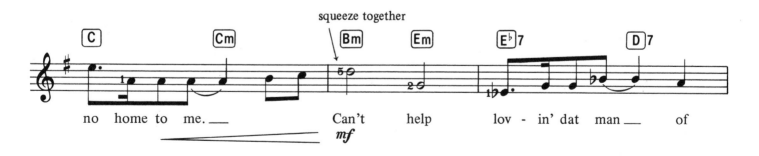

no home to me. Can't help lov - in' dat man of

mine.

27

OL' MAN RIVER

Music by Jerome Kern
Words by Oscar Hammerstein II

Suggested registration: clarinet
Rhythm: rhumba
Tempo: slow (♩ = 76)

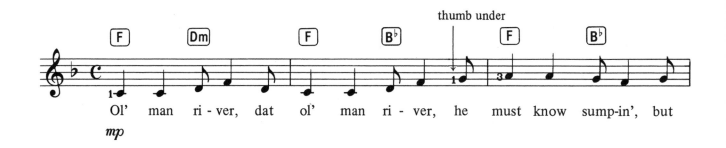

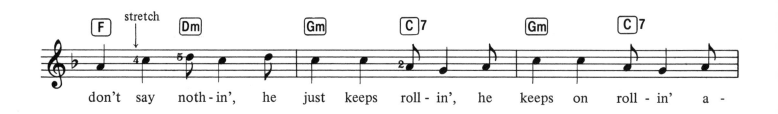

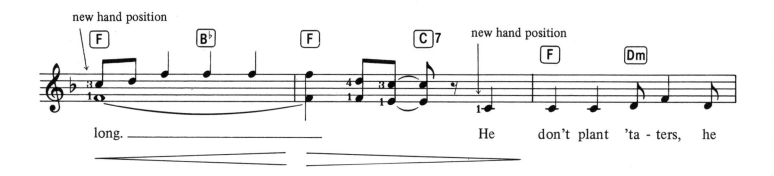

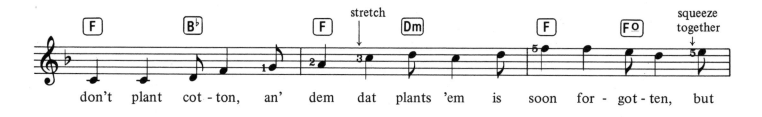

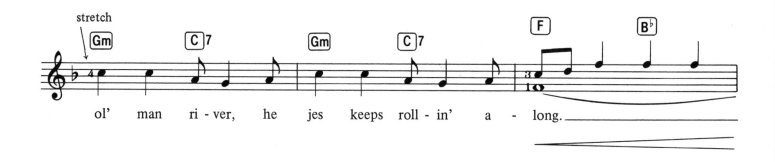

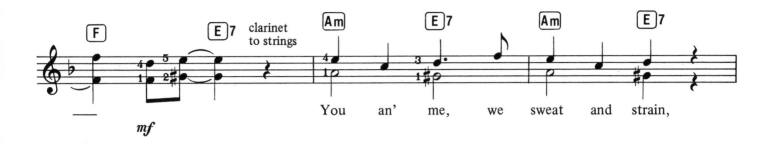

clarinet to strings

You an' me, we sweat and strain,

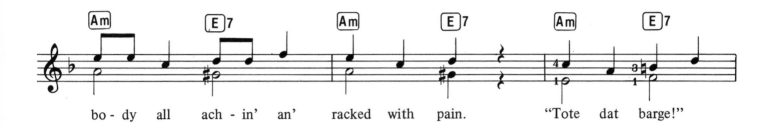

bo - dy all ach - in' an' racked with pain. "Tote dat barge!"

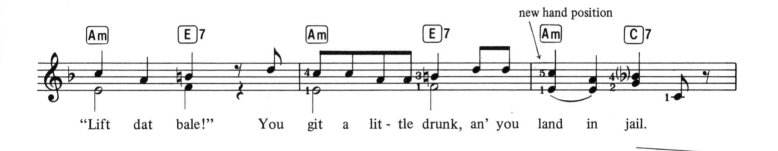

new hand position

"Lift dat bale!" You git a lit - tle drunk, an' you land in jail.

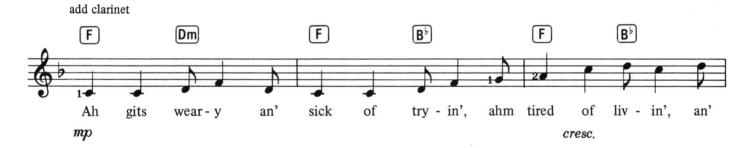

add clarinet

Ah gits wear - y an' sick of try - in', ahm tired of liv - in', an'

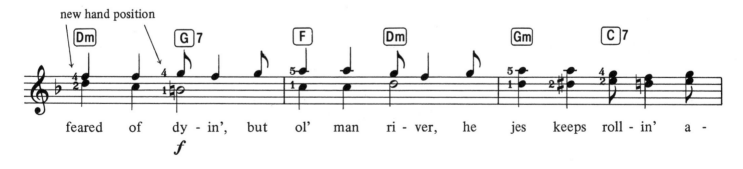

new hand position

feared of dy - in', but ol' man ri - ver, he jes keeps roll - in' a -

new hand position

long. stop rhythm

29

SMOKE GETS IN YOUR EYES

Music by Jerome Kern
Words by Otto Harbach

Suggested registration: piano
Rhythm: rhumba
Tempo: medium (♩ = 100)

So I chaffed____ them and I gai - ly laughed____ to think they could

mf

doubt my love. Yet to - day____ my love has

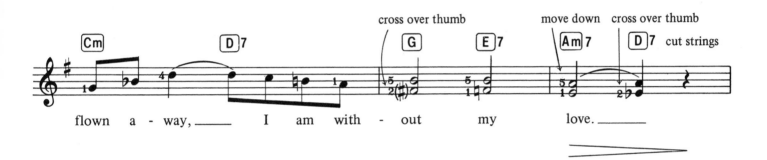

flown a - way,____ I am with - out my love.____

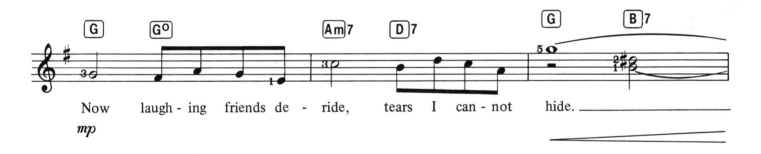

Now laugh - ing friends de - ride, tears I can - not hide.____

mp

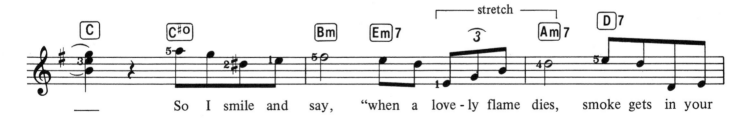

____ So I smile and say, "when a love - ly flame dies, smoke gets in your

eyes."

p

THE WAY YOU LOOK TONIGHT

Music by Jerome Kern
Words by Dorothy Fields

Suggested registration: oboe
Rhythm: rhumba
Tempo: fairly fast (♩ = 138)

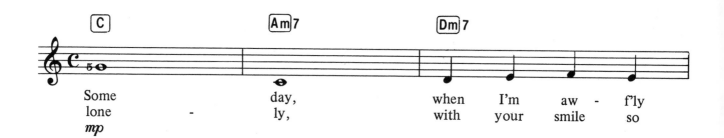

new hand position

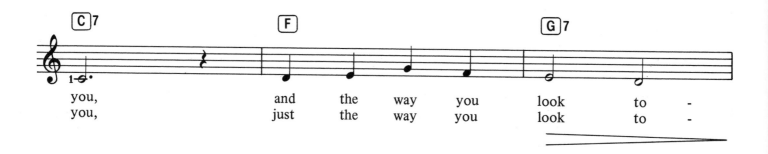

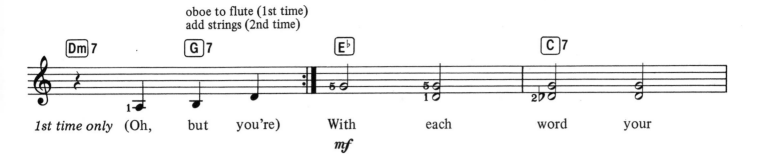

oboe to flute (1st time)
add strings (2nd time)

Dm7   G7   E♭   C7

1st time only (Oh,   but   you're)   With   each   word   your

mf

new hand position

Fm   B♭7   E♭

ten - der - ness   grows, _____   tear - ing   my   fear ___

G♭O   Fm   B♭7

___   a - part. _____

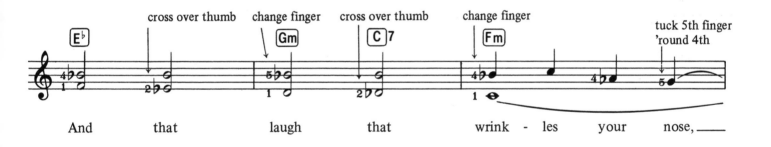

cross over thumb   change finger   cross over thumb   change finger   tuck 5th finger 'round 4th

E♭   Gm   C7   Fm

And   that   laugh   that   wrink - les   your   nose, ___

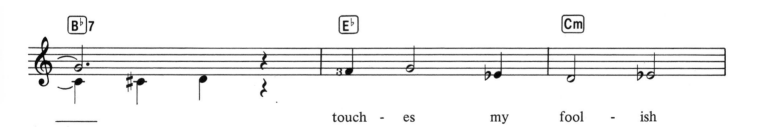

B♭7   E♭   Cm

____   touch - es   my   fool - ish

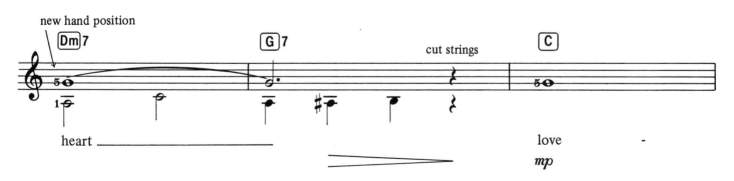

new hand position

Dm7   G7   cut strings   C

heart _____   love -

mp

33

ly,   ne - ver, ne - ver   change.

Keep   that   breath - less   charm,   won't   you   please   ar -

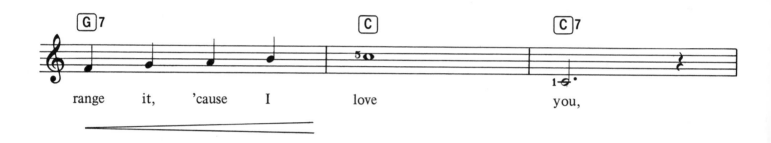

range   it,   'cause   I   love   you,

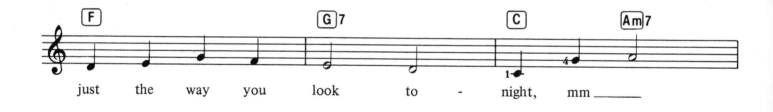

just   the   way   you   look   to   -   night,   mm _____

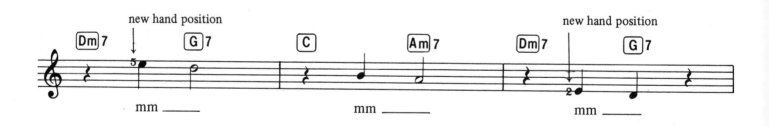

new hand position   new hand position

mm _____   mm _____   mm _____

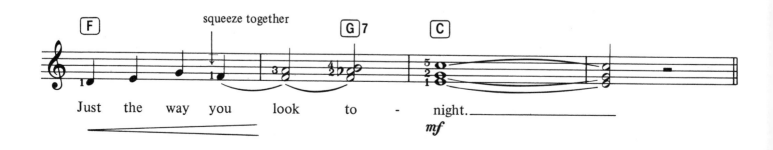

squeeze together

Just   the   way   you   look   to   -   night. _____
                                                mf

THE SONG IS YOU

Music by Jerome Kern
Words by Oscar Hammerstein II

Suggested registration: vibraphone
Rhythm: swing
Tempo: fairly fast (♩ = 152)

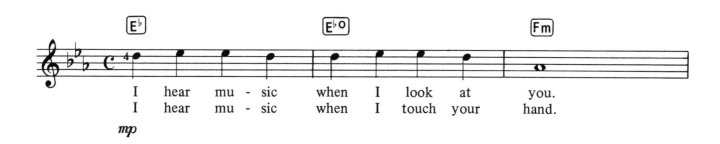

I hear mu - sic when I look at you.
I hear mu - sic when I touch your hand.

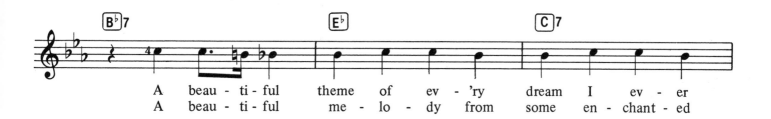

A beau - ti - ful theme of ev - 'ry dream I ev - er
A beau - ti - ful me - lo - dy from some en - chant - ed

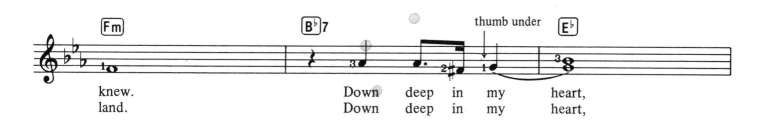

knew. Down deep in my heart,
land. Down deep in my heart,

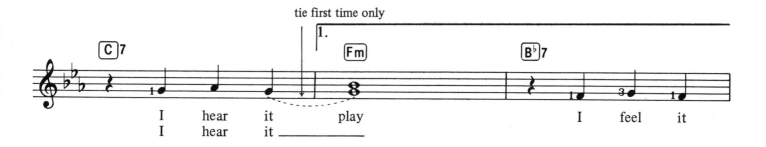

I hear it play
I hear it _____

I feel it

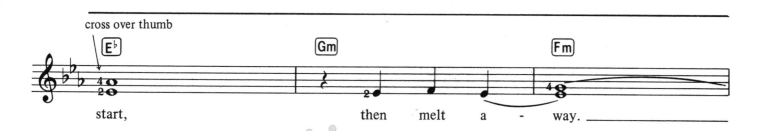

start, then melt a - way. _____

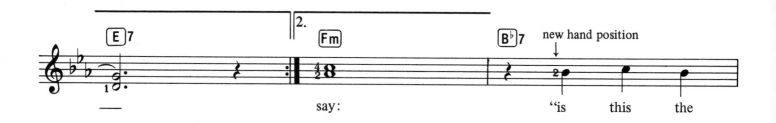

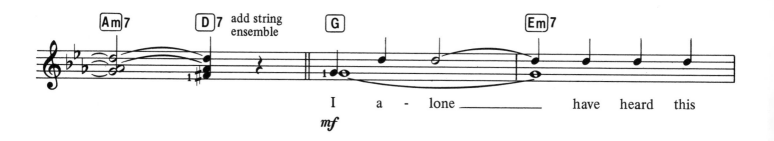

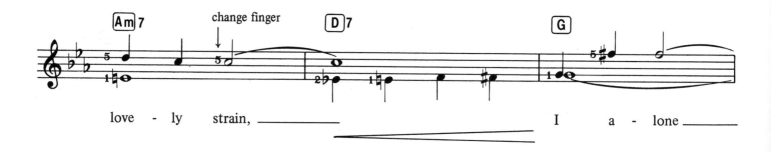

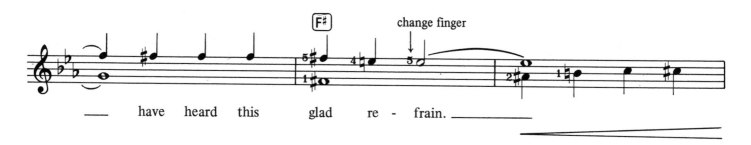

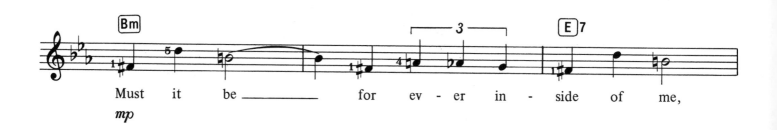

why can't I let it go? Why can't I
cresc.

let you know? Why can't I let you know the
mf

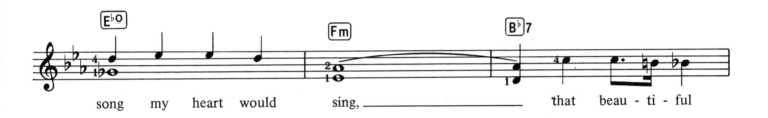

song my heart would sing, _____ that beau - ti - ful

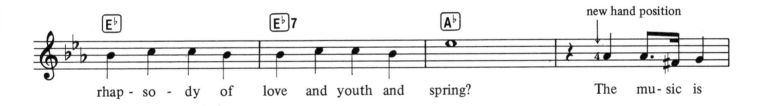

rhap - so - dy of love and youth and spring? The mu - sic is

sweet, _____ the words are true, _____ the song is

you. *f* stop rhythm

MASTER CHORD CHART

C

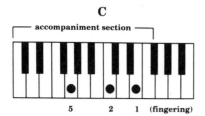

accompaniment section

5   2 1 (fingering)

Cm

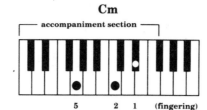

accompaniment section

5   2 1 (fingering)

C7

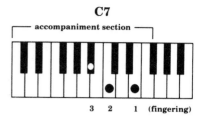

accompaniment section

3 2 1 (fingering)

D♭

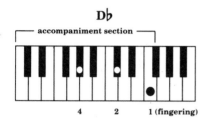

accompaniment section

4   2   1 (fingering)

C♯m

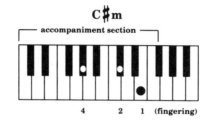

accompaniment section

4   2 1 (fingering)

D♭(C♯)7

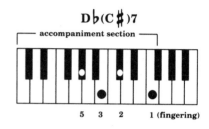

accompaniment section

5 3 2   1 (fingering)

D

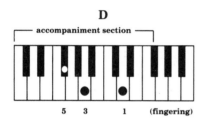

accompaniment section

5 3   1 (fingering)

Dm

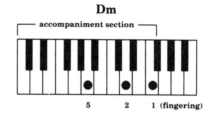

accompaniment section

5   2 1 (fingering)

D7

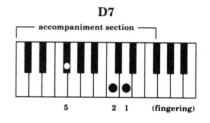

accompaniment section

5   2 1 (fingering)

E♭

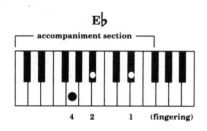

accompaniment section

4   2   1 (fingering)

E♭m

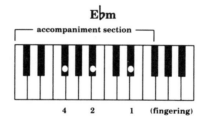

accompaniment section

4   2   1 (fingering)

E♭7

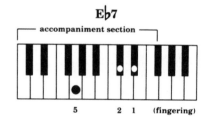

accompaniment section

5   2 1 (fingering)

E

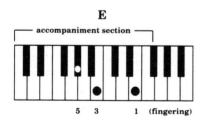

accompaniment section

5 3   1 (fingering)

Em

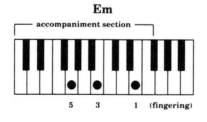

accompaniment section

5 3   1 (fingering)

E7

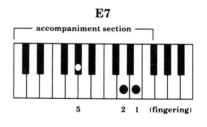

accompaniment section

5   2 1 (fingering)

F

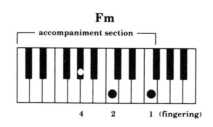

accompaniment section

4   2   1 (fingering)

Fm

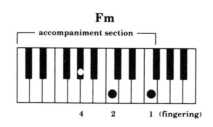

accompaniment section

4   2   1 (fingering)

F7

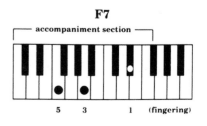

accompaniment section

5 3   1 (fingering)

MASTER CHORD CHART

G♭(F♯)

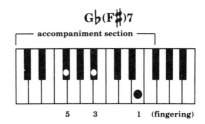

accompaniment section

5   3   1   (fingering)

F♯m

accompaniment section

5   3   1   (fingering)

G♭(F♯)7

accompaniment section

5   3   1   (fingering)

G

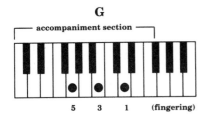

accompaniment section

5   3   1   (fingering)

Gm

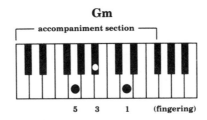

accompaniment section

5   3   1   (fingering)

G7

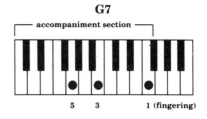

accompaniment section

5   3   1 (fingering)

A♭

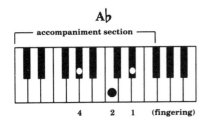

accompaniment section

4   2   1   (fingering)

A♭m

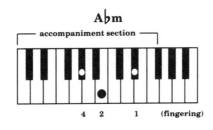

accompaniment section

4   2   1   (fingering)

A♭7

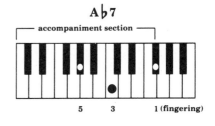

accompaniment section

5   3   1 (fingering)

A

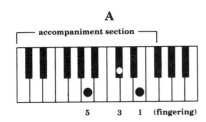

accompaniment section

5   3   1   (fingering)

Am

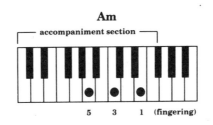

accompaniment section

5   3   1   (fingering)

A7

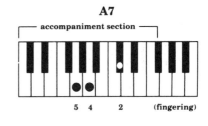

accompaniment section

5   4   2   (fingering)

B♭

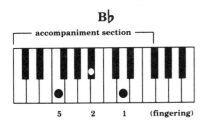

accompaniment section

5   2   1   (fingering)

B♭m

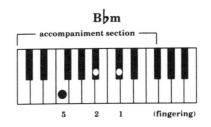

accompaniment section

5   2   1   (fingering)

B♭7

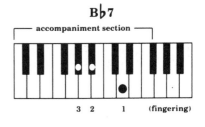

accompaniment section

3   2   1   (fingering)

B

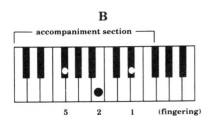

accompaniment section

5   2   1   (fingering)

Bm

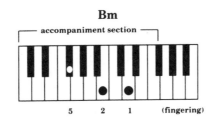

accompaniment section

5   2   1   (fingering)

B7

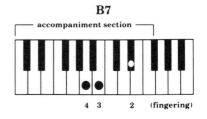

accompaniment section

4   3   2   (fingering)